Floppy had a bone.

1

A dog took the bone.

Floppy ran after the dog.

"Come back!" said Mum.

She ran after Floppy.

"Come back," said Dad.

He ran after Mum.

"Come back!" said Biff and Chip.

They ran after Dad.

The dog stopped.

A big dog took the bone.

The big dog ate the bone.
Oh no!